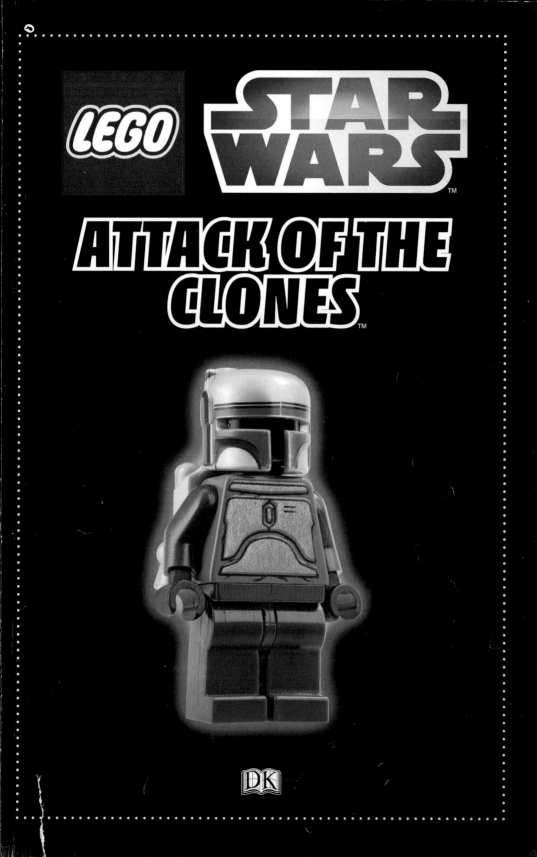

LONDON, NEW YORK, MUNICH,
MELBOURNE and DELHI

Editorial Assistant Ruth Amos
Senior Editor Elizabeth Dowsett
Designers Jon Hall, Sandra Perry
Pre-Production Producer Marc Staples
Producer Louise Daly
Publishing Manager Julie Ferris
Design Manager Nathan Martin
Art Director Ron Stobbart
Publishing Director Simon Beecroft

Reading Consultant
Maureen Fernandes

Dorling Kindersley would like to thank:
Randi Sørensen at the LEGO Group and J. W. Rinzler,
Leland Chee, Troy Alders and Carol Roeder at Lucasfilm.

First published in Great Britain in 2013 by
Dorling Kindersley Limited
80 Strand, London WC2R 0RL

10 9 8 7 6 5 4
004–187443–July/13

Page design copyright © 2014 Dorling Kindersley Limited

A CIP catalogue record for this book
is available from the British Library.

ISBN: 978-1-40933-484-2

Colour reproduction by Altaimage, UK
Printed and bound in China by L.Rex

Discover more at
www.dk.com
www.starwars.com
www.LEGO.com/starwars

Contents

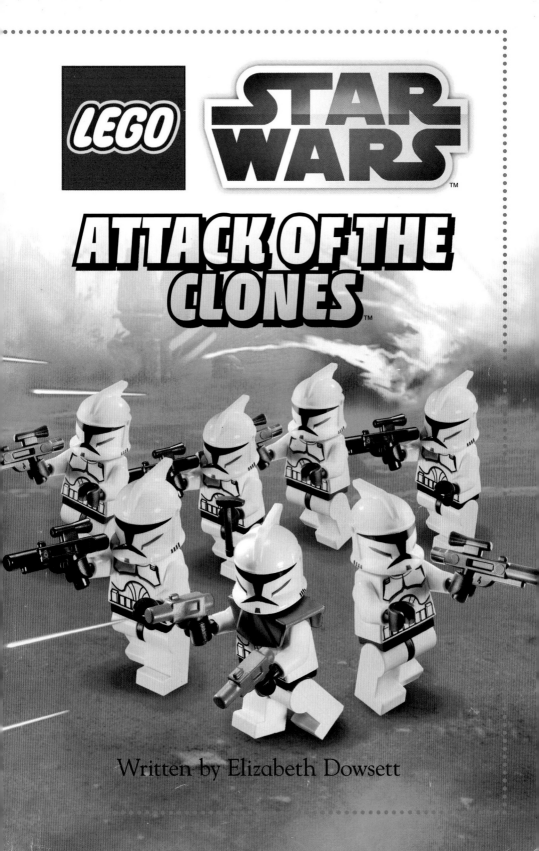

LEGO STAR WARS™

ATTACK OF THE CLONES™

Written by Elizabeth Dowsett

Trouble in the galaxy

Meet Count Dooku!

Once, Count Dooku protected the galaxy, but now he is a powerful Sith Lord.

The Sith are dangerous warriors who are greedy and want power.

Count Dooku leads an evil group called the Separatists.

The Separatists want to control the galaxy.

They will fight anyone who stands in their way.

Dark power

The Force is a form of energy. It can be used for good, but the Sith use the dark side of the Force for evil.

Welcome to the Jedi

These two Jedi are Obi-Wan Kenobi and Anakin Skywalker. The Jedi use the Force to protect the galaxy and keep peace.

Padawan braid

Obi-Wan Kenobi   **Anakin Skywalker**

Obi-Wan is a wise Jedi Master. He is Anakin's teacher.

Anakin is Obi-Wan's Padawan.
He is learning to be a Jedi Knight.
Count Dooku used to be a
Jedi, too, but now he has turned
against the Jedi Order.

When Jedi face an enemy, they
prefer to make peace than fight.
If they must do battle, they use
powerful lightsabers.

Lightsabers
These glowing weapons
are like swords, but they use
the power of the Force.

Jedi protection

Obi-Wan and Anakin have
an important Jedi mission.
They must protect Senator
Padmé Amidala on the planet
Coruscant.

Padmé may be in danger,
but she is not afraid!
She is very brave and daring.

The Senate

The Senate rules the Republic peacefully. The Senate is made up of a group of people who are called Senators.

Padmé and Anakin are childhood friends.

They are very happy to see each other after many years.

Zam Wesell's
green speeder

Assassin adventure

Help! Someone has tried
to attack Padmé.
Don't worry – Padmé is not hurt.

Obi-Wan and Anakin chase
after Padmé's attacker in a
yellow airspeeder.

Airspeeder

The Jedi are following an assassin called Zam Wesell. Before they catch Zam, someone destroys her.

Who destroyed Zam? The Jedi want to know!

Secret assassin
Assassins are paid to secretly track down and attack people.

The clone army

Look! Obi-Wan has found
a huge army of soldiers.

These soldiers are identical
to one another because they are
human clones.
They are all copied from one
man called Jango Fett.

Bounty hunter
Jango is a bounty hunter.
Bounty hunters are paid
to capture people.

Jango wears blue armour, but the clones wear white armour. Under the armour, the clone troopers all look like Jango.

The clone army will fight for the Republic, but it is a secret. Sshh! Don't tell anyone.

Stop that bounty hunter!

Obi-Wan has found out that
it was Jango Fett who destroyed
Zam Wesell.
Watch out, Obi-Wan!
Jango fires his blaster, but clever
Obi-Wan uses his lightsaber as
a shield.

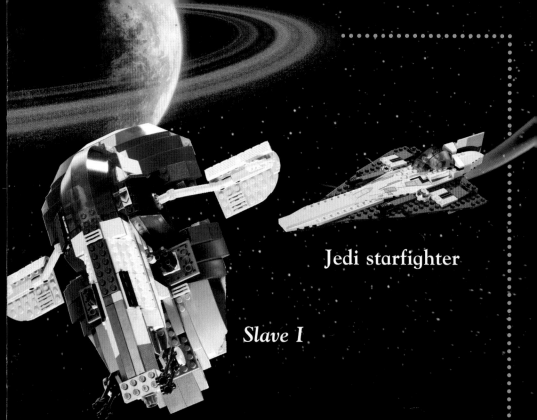

Jedi starfighter

Slave I

Jango escapes in his starship,
the *Slave I*. Whoosh!
Poor Obi-Wan doesn't like to fly,
but he chases after Jango in his
Jedi starfighter.
He follows Jango to a planet
called Geonosis.

The droid army

What is wicked Count Dooku up to now?
He is building an army of droids to fight for the Separatists!

The droids are metal soldiers.
The smaller, yellow droids are called battle droids.
They are not very clever.

Battle droid

Geonosians

The droid army is made by insect-like Geonosians. They have large wings and big eyes, like flies.

The bigger, silver droids are called super battle droids. They are strong and a little bit cleverer than battle droids. Beware the droid army!

Super battle droid

Dark secrets

Oh no! Count Dooku has found Obi-Wan on Geonosis and captured him! Energy beams keep Obi-Wan floating in a prison cell.

Count Dooku tells Obi-Wan that a clever Sith Lord has secretly taken control of the Republic.

Dooku reveals
that it was this
mysterious Sith
who planned
the attack
on Padmé
Amidala.

Obi-Wan
cannot move
his arms
or legs.
He is trapped!

Jedi to the rescue!

Anakin and Padmé come to save Obi-Wan, but the Separatists capture them, too!

More Jedi arrive, led by Jedi Master Mace Windu. The Jedi rescue their friends, but then the droid army attacks!

Mace Windu

Jedi strike team

Jedi warrior
Skilled Jedi Master Mace Windu defeats
Jango Fett with his purple lightsaber.
The bounty hunter is finished, but lots of
Separatists still want to fight.

The Jedi fight bravely, but
there are too many battle droids.
Help! The Jedi are surrounded.

Droid army

Republic
gunship

The Battle of Geonosis

Look! The clone troopers have arrived in a Republic gunship. They will rescue the Jedi!

The clone army launches an attack on the droids and the Geonosians, who fight back!

Geonosian cannon

Clone
speeder bike

AT-TE
walker

Spider droid

The droids have many
weapons, such as giant spider
droids and rolling hailfire droids.
The clone troopers fight bravely.

*Hailfire
droid*

Speeder bike

Geonosian guard

Dooku's escape

Who is this running away
from the battle?
It is cowardly Count Dooku,
fleeing on his speeder bike.
Quick, the villain will escape!

Obi-Wan and Anakin follow
Count Dooku to a secret hangar.

Anakin attacks the evil
Count, but he is overpowered.
Obi-Wan then fights Dooku
in a tense lightsaber battle,
but Dooku is too powerful.
All seems lost!

Lightning duel

A small green creature comes
to Anakin's rescue, just in time!
This is Yoda, Grand Master of
all the Jedi.
He might be very old and small,
but he is very powerful.
Do not judge him
by his size!

Yoda uses the
Force to leap
and spin
around Dooku.

Count Dooku attacks Yoda
with crackling Sith lightning,
but Yoda is strong enough to
bounce it back to him!

See the lightning flash!

Dooku's master

Count Dooku is powerful, but he is not as powerful as Yoda.

The Sith Lord knows he cannot win his duel against Yoda, so he runs away! Dooku uses his Solar Sailer spacecraft to fly to Coruscant.

Solar Sailer

Now Count Dooku has a secret meeting with a mysterious, cloaked figure.

This is Dooku's Sith master. He uses the dark side of the Force to hide his identity from the Jedi.

His name is Darth Sidious, but who is he? Where did he come from?

Time to celebrate!

The Battle of Geonosis is over and Count Dooku has fled! Also, Anakin and Padmé have fallen in love.

It is against the Jedi laws to get married, but they have a secret wedding.

C-3PO

Their droids, C-3PO and R2-D2, are the only guests.

The Jedi have won the battle this time, but the Clone Wars have only just begun.
Who is Darth Sidious and when will he strike next?

R2-D2

Quiz

1. What is this fly-like creature called?

2. What type of droid is this?

3. What is the name of Jango Fett's starship?

4. Who is this green warrior?

5. Who flees in the Solar Sailer spacecraft?

1. A Geonosian, 2. Super battle droid, 3. Slave I, 4. Yoda, 5. Count Dooku

Index